This book is dedicated to all the sailor moms
who are fierce and beautiful.

...and to my wonderful children.
ILYWPH&B

~tdf

my mommy is a sailor

ISBN 978-1-938505-36-2 ~ Paperback, February 2018
ISBN 978-1-938505-35-5 ~ Hardback, February 2018

Library of Congress Control Number: 2018934026

written and illustrated by
tahna desmond fox

my mommy is a
sailor

LIONHEART GROUP PUBLISHING ⚓ WWW.LIONHEARTGROUPPUBLISHING.COM

PRINTED IN THE USA ⚓ COLORADO

Yes, my mommy is a sailor
in the U.S. Navy.

She lives and works
aboard a ship
while docked or out at sea.

To be a sailor,
mommy trained for days
and months and years.

She learned the skills
and all the rules
to serve beside her peers.

Some mommies are
naval nurses,
while others fly the planes.

Some mommies guide ships
with radar through storms
of heavy rains.

Some mommies work
on destroyers,
while others work on subs.

I'm very proud of
my mommy
and everything she does.

All the sailors
aboard the ships
have many jobs to do.

They work all day
and every night
with members of their crew.

A job required
of the crew
to keep the ship secure,
each sailor stands
and guards their post.

That's what a 'watch' is for.

USS Ralph Johnson (DDG-114)

While my mom's ship
is underway,
she has to take her turn.

She watches for
signs of danger,
from ship's bow to its stern.

My mommy has
been teaching me ship
flags and what they mean.

The flags are hoisted
up the mast
in order to be seen.

15

16

Flags are used
to signal others
of dangers or distress.

Each flag has a
special meaning through
patterns they possess.

Sometimes my mom
is far away.
She has to go to sea.

She fights to secure
our freedom
and guard our liberty.

The best is when
she comes back home.
The sailors stand on deck.

We shout, "hello" and cheer
so loud because
we're glad she's back.

She tucks me in
my bed that night and
tells me of her trip.

Of all the things she
saw and did while
cruising on her ship.

USS Coronado (LCS-4)

She shares with me
her many tales of all
the sharks she saw.

I close my eyes and
picture them. Their teeth.
Their eyes. Their jaws.

When my mommy
prepares to leave,
she kisses me good-bye.

She hugs me tight,
says, "I love you"
as I try not to cry.

Yes, my mommy is a sailor.

Sometimes she has to go,
to protect her kin
and country,
and everyone we know.

TAHNA DESMOND FOX is a formally trained artist who has studied illustration and graphic design for a major portion of her adult life.

While typically a free-lance illustrator, this is her second self-authored and self-illustrated children's book. However, Mrs. Fox has had the privilege of illustrating many children's books for other amazing authors.

She currently resides wherever the U.S. Navy sees fit, with her sailor husband and two children.

Her family is her inspiration, as she continues on her colorful path of illustration and graphic design, as well as writing.

Other Works By Tahna Desmond Fox

Daddy's Boots

Momma's Boots

But... What If?

Grandpa, What If?

Don't Label Me

Stackable Paige

Oh, My! What Happened?

Sophe's on the Sofa

Squat, The Funny Little Inkblot

What Does a Hero Look Like?

Brooke, and her icky picky sister

My Daddy Sleeps Everywhere

my daddy is a sailor

Sebastian Earns His Stripes

CPSIA information can be obtained
at www.ICGtesting.com
Printed in the USA
LVHW07n1041090918
589607LV00012B/260/P